STANLE

GREAT BRITAIN
NUMBERS ISSUED
1840 to 1910

Compiled by RIKKI C. HYDE

STANLEY GIBBONS
London and Ringwood

"Happy is the man with a hobby for he has two worlds to live in"

(Rikki's adopted lifelong slogan)

When my book was first published in May, 1975 it created a storm of excitement as it enabled the collector for the first time to compare market prices of individual stamps with the rarity factor of numbers issued. Whilst the value of a stamp may also be influenced by its demand, its history and survival rate, and the quantities which were actually retrieved for collecting purposes, knowing the numbers issued gives the collector a good guide as to what is and what is not a reasonable buy at present price levels. For instance, a glance at the numbers issued for the 1887 Jubilee 4½d:' and the King Edward VII 7d. values may well surprise many collectors! Unfortunately, only 2000 of the 1975 edition of this book were printed. It soon became apparent that nowhere near enough copies had been produced to meet the demand of the many Great Britain collectors at that time and the book soon went out of print. In 1990 Stanley Gibbons offered to take over the publication and produced a second edition launched to coincide with the 1990 International Stamp Exhibition celebrating the 150th anniversary of the first postage stamp. Despite a larger quantity being produced even this eventually went out of print. Following many requests in recent years from present day collectors I am delighted that Stanley Gibbons has decided to publish a new third edition, this time in colour. I would like to dedicate this latest edition to the hobby of philately which has bestowed me with 55 years of pleasure as a collector and with 42 years of dedication as a dealer.

Rikki Hyde
March, 2008

CONTENTS

Stanley Gibbons Publications Ltd.
7 Parkside, Christchurch Road, Ringwood,
Hants. BH24 3SH
Published by
Stanley Gibbons Publications Ltd.
Editorial, Sales Offices
and Distribution Centre,
7 Parkside, Christchurch Road,
Ringwood, Hants BH24 3SH.

First published in 1975 by Birmingham and Bristol Stamp Auctions Ltd.

© Stanley Gibbons Publications Ltd., 2008

ISBN 13 978-0-85259-695-1
ISBN 10 0-85259-695-2

Printed & Bound by
Butler & Tanner, Frome, Somerset.

INTRODUCTION

My fortunate discovery some years ago of the rare Great Britain error of the 1883 6d on 6d, overprint double (S.G.162L), first made me think in terms of calculating rarity value from numbers issued. Just six years ago I started to compile and collate information regarding numbers issued, printed, or sold for the Victorian era, and later I extended this to the Edwardian period. This was purely for my own use, and I had no intention at that time of producing a publication. Many basic figures were first gained from the Robson Lowe Encyclopaedia, for which I express my sincere gratitude and from thereon I collated information from numerous publications, articles, and official records, all of which helped me to compile what is now an almost complete listing. My appreciation is extended to all those people whose painstaking research in these articles have helped me to produce this catalogue.

To the best of my knowledge, a combined listing dedicated to numbers issued for Victorian and Edwardian stamps of Great Britain in catalogue form has never before been published. The object of this work is to enable its users to assess rarity value and to be able to judge for themselves what is and what is not a good buy. Indeed, many amusing anomalies appear when comparing this listing with any standard priced catalogue!

The statistics in this catalogue for 'numbers issued' relate to those put into circulation, sold, or printed, whichever is the most realistic figure available. The quantities are often qualified by notes on printing spoilage or numbers officially destroyed. In some cases, where figures were not fully available, an estimated or calculated approximate number has been entered. Whilst all the quantities and data are entered in this catalogue in all good faith, I can neither guarantee their accuracy nor accept responsibility for errors.

It must be remembered that survival rate plays a large part in determining rarity. Obviously, one cannot lay down a set survival rate for every stamp, but about 2% can generally be used as a gauge for calculating possible numbers in existence for this period (say 5 to each sheet of 240). Furthermore, even the survival rate includes both mint and used examples, and generally there are at least 50 used examples for every mint copy in existence (with the exception perhaps of the 1887 Jubilee 4½). The earlier Victorian also had 240 different letter combinations to each sheet, and this should be considered by those who are attempting reconstructions. Some of the later Victorian (and a few of the earlier ones) and Edwardian were overprinted for use as 'Officials' and for use in other countries. This too should be taken into consideration, and a tabulated listing of the stamps involved and some statistical figures are given at the end of this book.

With all these points in mind, let us take an example of the sort of calculation that can be derived from this catalogue:

Mr. X is reconstructing by letters the 1876 8d orange in used condition, and is searching for one more letter combination to complete his set. He calculates his chances of finding it as follows:

Total number issued	4,800,000	
Survival rate 2%	50)	4,800,000
i.e. divide by 50 =		96,000
Less mint survival rate 1/50th		1,920
Fraction of Letter Combination	240)	94,080
i.e. divide by 240 =		392

Mr.X would probably be looking for one of 392 copies in existence. Thus, each used 8d orange should have a letter combination rarity value of 1/392th. Let us assume for the purpose of this exercise that a unique stamp is worth £3,000 (based on the auction realisation of the 1867 10d plate 2, mint), then Mr. X should expect to pay 1/392ths of £3,000 for it (i.e. about £8). This, of course, does not take 'condition' into account, but the condition does not alter the rarity value, but only reduces the price for an inferior specimen.

When King Edward VII died on the 6th of May 1910, Messrs. De La Rue passed over some of the printing plates to Messrs. Harrison & Sons and to the Somerset House Printers, but unfortunately from then on, it appears that inadequate records were kept of the numbers of stamps issued or produced. For this reason I regret my book finishes at 1910. However, records were kept for commemorative sets from 1924 and those issued to the end of the reign of King George VI have been listed by me, but because most specialised catalogues list the numbers sold for the Queen Elizabeth period, I feel it is pointless repeating them here.

I wish success to all the users of my book, and I dedicate this work to my beloved hobby of stamp collecting and to all those who collect the stamps of Great Britain.

Rikki C. Hyde
BRISTOL,
January 1st, 1975

GENERAL INFORMATION

FORMAT
Stamps are listed in a suitable order to allow easy cross-reference with most published standard priced catalogues. Illustrations are provided for quick identification. The total number issued is given for each stamp disregarding plate numbers and this is usually followed by a more detailed break-down of the various plates and any relevant notes.

SHADES, PAPER AND VARIETIES
Most shades are caused by variation in the pigment of printers' ink and do not form separate issues. These and minor varieties of paper, watermark, gum, printing and imperforate errors of perforated issues are beyond the scope of this catalogue.

PERFORATION
The first issues from 1840 were imperforate. Line-engraved stamps of 1848 to 1858 were perforated either 14 or 16. The later line-engraved and all surface-printed issues were perforated 14 with the exception of the 1867 Maltese Cross Watermark high values. Where a perforation is not indicated in the text, it must be taken as being gauge 14.

WATERMARKS
The following are the watermarks used during the period covered:

Small Crown   Large Crown   'Halfpenny'   V. R.

Small Garter   Medium Garter   Large Garter   Emblems   Spray of Rose

Maltese Cross   Large Anchor   Small Anchor   Orb   Imperial Crown

The Essential Guide To The Line Engraved 1840 To 1864 1d & 2d Stars

For each plate used, Dr Statham analyses its HISTORY, ALIGNMENT, CHARACTERISTICS, CHECK LETTERS, DESCRIPTION, DATES, QUANTITIES, IMPRIMATURS and gives detailed listings of its VARIETIES and an aid to PLATING. The impetus for this book came from the frustration in his early plating days with the information then published. The availability and access to the new information, material and original documents has enabled previous data to be checked and amended where necessary. Many THOUSANDS of NEW VARIETIES have been listed for the first time, following Dr. Statham's meticulous research and process of double-checking. It is intended that virtually EVERY VARIETY is ILLUSTRATED - all drawn by Dr. Statham.

Dr. Statham hoped that his publication would enable other collectors, both specialist and beginners alike, to derive the same pleasure that he has had over the years in collecting these issues. As the scope of the book is so large, it has been published in several parts and with the publication of Volume 18 and totals 3835 pages.

For a limited period we are able to offer Full Sets of this amazing publication with each section in a superb Presentation Box for just £950, with an extended payment facility of 6 months and Free Postage within the UK.

We specialize in the Line Engraved 1840 To 1864 1d & 2d SG1 to SG42

We have good stocks of IMPERFS, PERFS & PLATES, both UNPLATED and PLATED including the RARE PLATES 175, 176 and 177 IMPERF with R.RS. certificates as well as The GARDINER-HILL Collection of the First Perforated Issue and INVERTED WMKS from the whole range.

Reflecting our COMPREHENSIVE stocks of GB, QV to KGVI They include our specialist areas mentioned above as well as:-

LISTS

1) SG 43/44 Id RED PLATES with CDS postmarks
2) Queen Victoria Surface-Printed to KGVI CDs & mint
3) GREAT BRITAIN USED ABROAD
4) INDIVIDUALLY PLATED 1d RED IMPERFS & STARS
5) A RARE, UNUSUAL and DIFFICULT-TO-FIND section
ALL STAMPS ARE ILLUSTRATED

LISTS

Website:
www.ericpaul.co.uk
Email: info@ericpaul.co.uk

Eric Paul Ltd.
PO BOX 44, MARPLE
CHESHIRE SK6 7EE

Tel No. 0161 427 2101
Fax No. 0161 427 6386
Postal Only

VISA

Members: P.T.S.   M.&D.P.T.A.   G.B.P.S.   A.D.P.S.

PLATE NUMBERS
These are listed separately for stamps which incorporate the plate number in their design, and also for the earlier 1d Blacks and 2d Blues, but not for the 1d Red 'stars' owing to their complexity.

OFFICIAL STAMPS, AND BRITISH STAMPS OVERPRINTED FOR USE IN OTHER COUNTRIES
Tabulated listing of stamps overprinted for these purposes will be found at the end of the catalogue, together with some information on numbers overprinted.

POST–1910 PERIOD
For convenience, numbers issued for commemorative sets up to the end of the reign of King George VI have been included.

All stamps were issued in sheets of 240 unless otherwise stated

QUEEN VICTORIA Line-Engraved Issues

1840 1d BLACK
Watermark Small Crown – Imperforate
Total number issued 68,158,080 (283,992 sheets)

Break-down of plates:

Plate la	4,133,760	(17,224 sheets)
1b	5,918,640	(24,661 sheets)
2	7,659,120	(31,913 sheets)
3	4,786,800	(19,945 sheets)
4	6,701,760	(27,924 sheets)
5	8,616,480	(35,902 sheets)
6	9,095,040	(37,896 sheets)
7	8,137,680	(33,907 sheets)
8	7,180,320	(29,918 sheets)
9	3,840,000	(16,000 sheets)
10	1,920,000	(8,000 sheets)
11	168,000	(700 sheets)

In addition, 8,453 sheets (2,028,720 stamps) were produced but spoilt in printing and were officially destroyed.
Notes: The total number of 1d Blacks distributed in 1840 is recorded as 63,561,840.
The figure for plate 1a does not include spoilage. The plate 1b figure includes spoilage for both 1a and 1b.
Owing to the deficiency of black obliterating ink for the superseding 1d Red stamps, a late consignment of black stamps was printed and delivered in January/February, 1841 which amounted to 10,018 sheets (2,404,320 stamps). This provisional printing included all plates save plates '2' and '8', whilst the scarce Plate '11' was only introduced at this stage. The above totals include this late provisional printing and of the 8,453 spoilt sheets, 182 sheets were from this printing.

1840 2d BLUE
Watermark Small Crown – Imperforate
Total number issued 6,462,960 (26,929 sheets)

Break-down of plates:

Plate 1	3,977,280	(16,572 sheets)
2	2,485,680	(10,357 sheets)

In addition, 633 sheets (151,920 stamps) were produced of the combined plates but spoilt in printing and were officially destroyed. **Notes:** The total number of 2d Blues recorded as sold in 1840 is 5,382,240.

The first delivery of 2d Blues was not until 8th May, 1840 (two days after the issue of the 1d Black) and this consisted of only 600 sheets which were restricted to sale within the London area.

1841 1d RED

Watermark Small Crown – Imperforate
Total number issued over 2,588,000,000 of which it is estimated 120,000,000 were later perforated, leaving an approximate total of imperforate stamps of 2,468,000,000.
Break-down of plates: About four-fifths of this quantity (over 2,013,000,000 stamps) were from plates 1 to 131 of Alphabet I and the remainder (about 575,000,000 stamps) were from plates 132 to 175 of Alphabet II. Some of the latter group, i.e. Alphabet II, were later perforated (see above) and these perforated types are included in the totals for the 1854–61 issue.
Notes: The first delivery of red stamps was made by the 27th of January, 1841 and consisted of some 19,000 sheets printed from the original black plates 1, 2, 5, 8, 9, 10 and the new plate 11.

A Trial Printing of plate 11 on Dickinson silk-threaded paper was made in April, 1841 consisting of 8 sheets (1920 stamps), six sheets being gummed and two without gum.

1841 2d BLUE

Watermark Small Crown – Imperforate
Total number issued about 87,960,000 (366,500 sheets)

Break-down of plates:

Plate 3	45,960,000	(191,500 sheets)
4	42,000,000	(175,000 sheets)

Notes: The later perforated issue of plate 4 was from a new printing with the marginal inscriptions altered and not from remainders of the imperforate sheets.

1848–53 1d RED WITH "TRIAL PERFORATIONS"

Henry Archer apparently experimented on 5,000 sheets (1,200,000 stamps) with his perforating machines between 1848 to 1850, most of which were destroyed because of imperfections. A similar quantity was used by the Government in 1853 whilst making trial perforations (gauge 14 and 16) on the Napier Machine.

1854–61 PERFORATED 1d REDS

Total number issued for the combined Large and Small Crown watermarked paper perforated 14 or 16 was over 5,116,000,000 (21,316,500+ sheets). Unfortunately, figures are not available for the separate issues except that for the 1854 1d Die I on Small Crown paper perforated 16 well in excess of 410,000,000 (1,708,300+ sheets) were produced, and it is estimated that some 3,840,000,000 (16,000,000 sheets) were on white paper. Consequently, the remaining issues could only have totalled less than 866,000,000 (3,608,300 sheets) altogether.
Break-down of plates: This varies considerably. For instance, only 19,400 sheets were printed of plate 64, whilst plate 27 produced over a million sheets on white paper alone.

1854–58 PERFORATED 2d BLUES

Total number issued for the combined Large and Small Crown watermarked paper perforated 14 or 16 was about 45,360,000 (189,000 sheets).

Break-down of plates and issues:

Small Crown perf. 16

(plate 4)	14,160,000	(59,000 sheets)
(plate 5)	960,000	(4,000 sheets)

Small Crown perf. 14

(plate 4)	1,680,000	(7,000 sheets)
(plate 5)	1,920,000	(8,000 sheets)

Large Crown perf. 16

(plate 5)	960,000	(4,000 sheets)

Large Crown perf. 14

(plate 5)	15,600,000	(65,000 sheets)
(plate 6)	8,880,000	(37,000 sheets)

Large Crown perf. 16 on white paper

(plate 6)	1,200,000	(5,000 sheets)

1858–69 1d RED WITH LETTERS IN ALL FOUR CORNERS

Watermark Large Crown – Plate Numbers printed in the design
Total number issued 13,434,000,000 (55,975,000 sheets)

Break-down of plates printed including spoilt sheets:

Plate 71	133,680,000	(557,000 sheets)
72	125,472,000	(552,800 sheets)
73	127,176,000	(529,900 sheets)
74	127,440,000	(531,000 sheets)
76	133,320,000	(555,500 sheets)
78	147,744,000	(615,600 sheets)
79	153,264,000	(638,600 sheets)
80	118,848,000	(495,200 sheets)
81	124,872,000	(520,300 sheets)
82	63,216,000	(263,400 sheets)
83	47,904,000	(199,600 sheets)
84	88,656,000	(369,400 sheets)
85	122,472,000	(510,300 sheets)
86	110,520,000	(460,500 sheets)
87	110,976,000	(462,400 sheets)
88	47,760,000	(199,000 sheets)
89	120,936,000	(503,900 sheets)
90	113,208,000	(471,700 sheets)
91	92,184,000	(384,100 sheets)
92	136,248,000	(567,700 sheets)
93	109,224,000	(455,100 sheets)
94	114,864,000	(478,600 sheets)
95	128,064,000	(533,600 sheets)
96	117,192,000	(488,300 sheets)
97	128,832,000	(536,800 sheets)
98	84,336,000	(351,400 sheets)
99	85,272,000	(355,300 sheets)
100	61,608,000	(256,700 sheets)
101	89,400,000	(372,500 sheets)
102	118,848,000	(495,200 sheets)
103	96,144,000	(400,600 sheets)

104	42,336,000	(176,400 sheets)
105	48,624,000	(202,600 sheets)
106	93,912,000	(391,300 sheets)
107	77,040,000	(321,000 sheets)
108	51,240,000	(213,500 sheets)
109	56,760,000	(236,500 sheets)
110	76,032,000	(316,800 sheets)
111	108,648,000	(452,700 sheets)
112	71,856,000	(299,400 sheets)
113	87,840,000	(366,000 sheets)
114	55,944,000	(233,100 sheets)
115	51,360,000	(214,000 sheets)
116	84,120,000	(350,500 sheets)
117	114,960,000	(479,000 sheets)
118	105,792,000	(440,800 sheets)
119	118,512,000	(493,800 sheets)
120	169,632,000	(706,800 sheets)
121	97,488,000	(406,200 sheets)
122	166,416,000	(693,400 sheets)
123	107,472,000	(447,800 sheets)
124	143,448,000	(597,700 sheets)
125	103,128,000	(429,700 sheets)
127	94,872,000	(395,300 sheets)
129	104,352,000	(434,800 sheets)
130	98,880,000	(412,000 sheets)
131	76,968,000	(320,700 sheets)
132	22,872,000	(95,300 sheets)
133	33,936,000	(141,400 sheets)
134	190,368,000	(793,200 sheets)
135	45,720,000	(190,500 sheets)
136	71,880,000	(299,500 sheets)
137	143,088,000	(596,200 sheets)
138	168,072,000	(700,300 sheets)
139	46,632,000	(194,300 sheets)
140	235,800,000	(982,500 sheets)
141	43,512,000	(181,300 sheets)
142	50,952,000	(212,300 sheets)
143	68,808,000	(286,700 sheets)
144	49,584,000	(206,600 sheets)
145	130,800,000	(545,000 sheets)
146	110,424,000	(460,100 sheets)
147	99,192,000	(413,300 sheets)
148	121,872,000	(507,800 sheets)
149	113,976,000	(474,900 sheets)
150	163,800,000	(682,500 sheets)
151	67,872,000	(282,800 sheets)
152	77,496,000	(322,900 sheets)
153	30,816,000	(128,400 sheets)
154	99,624,000	(415,100 sheets)
155	92,472,000	(385,300 sheets)
156	119,232,000	(496,800 sheets)
157	108,000,000	(450,000 sheets)
158	127,440,000	(531,000 sheets)
159	117,528,000	(489,700 sheets)
160	126,000,000	(525,000 sheets)

161	55,752,000	(232,300 sheets)
162	87,648,000	(365,200 sheets)
163	90,552,000	(377,300 sheets)
164	76,392,000	(318,300 sheets)
165	115,992,000	(483,300 sheets)
166	92,352,000	(384,800 sheets)
167	119,376,000	(497,400 sheets)
168	89,832,000	(374,300 sheets)
169	55,944,000	(233,100 sheets)
170	137,400,000	(572,500 sheets)
171	217,608,000	(906,700 sheets)
172	110,064,000	(458,600 sheets)
173	72,792,000	(303,300 sheets)
174	108,000,000	estimate
175	90,456,000	(376,900 sheets)
176	76,144,000	(313,100 sheets)
177	90,000,000	estimate
178	58,944,000	(245,600 sheets)
179	97,824,000	(407,600 sheets)
180	51,720,000	(215,500 sheets)
181	114,864,000	(478,600 sheets)
182	51,648,000	(215,200 sheets)
183	90,384,000	(376,600 sheets)
184	70,000,000	estimate
185	53,112,000	(221,300 sheets)
186	73,056,000	(304,400 sheets)
187	102,672,000	(427,800 sheets)
188	55,584,000	(231,600 sheets)
189	52,320,000	(218,000 sheets)
190	80,000,000	estimate
191	80,000,000	estimate
192	110,400,000	(460,000 sheets)
193	80,000,000	estimate
194	66,000,000	(275,000 sheets)
195	72,000,000	estimate
196	78,000,000	estimate
197	61,728,000	(257,200 sheets)
198	96,000,000	estimate
199	75,360,000	(314,000 sheets)
200	65,000,000	estimate
201	83,448,000	(347,700 sheets)
202	60,000,000	estimate
203	96,000,000	estimate
204	85,000,000	estimate
205	85,000,000	estimate
206	92,000,000	estimate
207	60,000,000	estimate
208	85,000,000	estimate
209	85,000,000	estimate
210	45,384,000	(189,100 sheets)
211	34,000,000	estimate
212	60,000,000	estimate
213	60,000,000	estimate
214	55,000,000	estimate
215	55,000,000	estimate

216	48,000,000	estimate
217	36,000,000	estimate
218	37,000,000	estimate
219	12,000,000	estimate
220	37,000,000	estimate
221	31,000,000	estimate
222	30,000,000	estimate
223	15,000,000	estimate
224	20,000,000	estimate
225	3,000,000	estimate

The total number printed for plates 71 to 225 amounted to about 14,000,000,000 stamps (58,333,000 sheets) of which some 566,000,000 stamps (2,358,000 sheets) were spoilt in printing and officially destroyed, leaving a total number actually issued of 13,434,000,000 stamps (55,975,000 sheets).

Notes: Plate '77' (together with plates 69, 70, 75, 126 and 128) was rejected owing to defects, but a few sheets were apparently printed from which seven or eight stamps have survived.

1858–69 2d BLUE WITH LETTERS IN ALL FOUR CORNERS
Watermark Large Crown – Plate Numbers printed in the design
Total number issued about 196,824,000 (820,100 sheets.

Break-down of plates:

Plate 7	9,600,000	(40,000 sheets)
8	15,840,000	(66,000 sheets)
9	92,040,000	(383,500 sheets)
12	7,344,000	(30,600 sheets)
13	30,000,000	(125,000 sheets)
14	21,000,000	estimate
15	21,000,000	estimate

Notes: No official records were kept of numbers printed or issued for plates 14 or 15. However, accepting that these two plates are of comparable rarity, we have arrived at the above estimates by dividing equally the remainder after deducting the quantities known for the other plates from the total number issued.

1870 ½d RED
Watermark 'Halfpenny' extending over three stamps. Issued in sheets of 480
Total number issued 1,600,276,320 (3,333,909 sheets)
In addition, 236,923,680 (493,591 sheets) were produced but spoilt in printing and were officially destroyed.

Break-down of plates printed including spoilt sheets:

Plate 1	58,320,000	(121,500 sheets)
3	92,400,000	(192,500 sheets)
4	127,008,000	(264,600 sheets)
5	255,936,000	(533,200 sheets)
6	193,008,000	(402,100 sheets)
8	12,500,000	estimate
9	2,500,000	estimate
10	185,328,000	(386,100 sheets)
11	197,280,000	(411,000 sheets)
12	175,000,000	estimate
13	175,000,000	estimate
14	175,000,000	estimate

15	80,000,000	estimate
19	60,000,000	estimate
20	48,000,000	estimate

1870 1½d RED
Watermark Large Crown
Total number issued 42,638,160 (177,659 sheets)
In addition, 2,874,000 (11,975 sheets) were produced but spoilt in printing and were officially destroyed.

Break-down of plates printed including spoilt sheets:

Plate 1 (no plate number)	15,872,160	(66,134 sheets)
3 (number 3 at sides)	29,640,000	(123,500 sheets)

This stamp was prepared for use in 1860 but not issued and 10,000 sheets (2,400,000 stamps) of plate 1 were printed in rosy-mauve. Of these, 1,000 sheets were overprinted "Specimen" and distributed to postmasters. Of the remaining 9,000 sheets, 8,962 were destroyed in May, 1867. The remaining 38 sheets (9,120 stamps) have since been split up and are in the hands of collectors.

The error of lettering OP-PC instead of CP-PC occurred on all printings from plate 1, thus 66,134 examples (one on each sheet) were originally created. However, since the error was not discovered until 1894 many of these must have been destroyed.

Embossed Stamps

1847 1s GREEN
Paper with silk threads – Imperforate – Issued in sheets of 20
Total number issued 5,655,420 (282,771 sheets)
In addition, 1,804,580 (90,229 sheets) were produced but spoilt in printing and were officially destroyed.

Break-down of Dies (estimated):

Die I	3,000,000	(150,000 sheets)
Die II	2,655,420	(132,771 sheets)

Notes: The first printing was in 1847 when 40,000 sheets were printed. Subsequent printings were not until 1850 (16,000 sheets), 1851 (32,000 sheets), 1852 (46,000 sheets), 1853 (64,000 sheets), and the remainder were printed prior to the end of October, 1856.

1848 10d BROWN
Paper with silk threads – Imperforate – Issued in sheets of 24
Total number issued 2,805,960 (116,915 sheets)
In addition, 122,040 (5,085 sheets) were produced which are believed to have been destroyed as waste, making a total printing of 122,000 sheets.

Break-down of Dies:

Die I	404,016	(16,834 sheets)
Die II	826,104	(34,421 sheets)
Die III	1,382,736	(57,614 sheets)
Die IV	193,104	(8,046 sheets)

Notes: The first printing was in 1847 when 20,000 sheets were printed. Subsequent printings were not until 1850 (8,000 sheets), 1851 (16,000 sheets), 1852 (14,000 sheets), 1853 (32,000 sheets), 1854 (32,000 sheets).

The 10d was withdrawn on August 15th, 1855 but re-issued in 1862 when 2,012 withdrawn sheets, left over at Somerset House, were put back into circulation.

1854 6d PURPLE

Watermark 'V.R.' – Imperforate – Issued in sheets of 40
Total number issued 3,718,280 (92,957 sheets)
Of 6,659,920 (166,498 sheets) printed, which included 2,219,920 (55,498 sheets) printed in 1856 but never issued, 2,941,640 (73,541 sheets) were apparently officially destroyed upon the introduction of the surface-printed 6d.

Notes: 4,000 of the total number issued were overprinted "Specimen" and distributed amongst various post offices.

Surface-Printed Issues

1855 4d CARMINE

Watermark Small Garter – Thick, blued 'Safety' paper
Total number issued 2,770,800 (11,545 sheets)

Break-down of plates:

Plate 1	2,760,000	(11,500 sheets)
2	10,800	(45 sheets)

Notes: The quantity of plate 1 includes a late printing made in November, 1856 and January, 1857 on a remainder stock of Small Garter watermarked paper which lacked the blueing giving the appearance of white paper and we estimate these amounted to 1,000 sheets. The quantity of plate 2 includes the imprimatur sheet.

4,000 stamps from plate 1 were overprinted "Specimen" and distributed amongst various post offices.

1856 4d CARMINE

Watermark Medium Garter – Thick, blued `Safety' paper.
Total number issued 1,320,000 (5,500 sheets)
Break-down of plates: All plate 1.

1856 4d CARMINE ON WHITE PAPER

Watermark Medium Garter
Total number issued 480,000 (2,000 sheets)
Break-down of plates: All plate 1.

1856 4d ROSE

Watermark Medium Garter – Specially prepared ink
Total number issued 1,800,000 (7,500 sheets)
Break-down of plates: All plate 1.

1857 4d ROSE

Watermark Large Garter
Total number issued 28,776,960 (119,904 sheets)

Break-down of plates:

Plate 1	23,147,760	(96,449 sheets)
2	5,629,200	(23,455 sheets)

1856 6d LILAC

Watermark Emblems
Total number issued 32,040,000 (133,500 sheets)
Break-down of plates: All plate 1.
Notes: The first 2,000 sheets (480,000 stamps) were printed on azure paper.

1856 1s GREEN
Watermark Emblems
Total number issued 12,120,000 (50,500 sheets)
Break-down of plates: All plate 1.
Notes: The first 500 sheets (120,000 stamps) were printed earlier by way of an experiment on azure paper in June 1856.

1862–64 SERIES WITH `SMALL WHITE CORNER LETTERS'
Watermark Emblems (except 4d which has Large Garter)

3d CARMINE-ROSE
Total number issued 5,173,200 (21,555 sheets)

Break-down of plates:

Plate 2	5,172,000	(21,550 sheets)
3	1,200	(5 sheets)

Notes: The 3d plate 2 was first printed with a network background in the spandrels. These were never issued and consisted of 1,458 sheets which were mainly destroyed, but a few were overprinted "Specimen" and some exist without the overprint. These are not included in the quantities given.

The 3d plate 3 were the five Registration sheets of which one or two sheets were perforated and put into circulation. A few used copies (two of which came from Yarmouth) and 2 unused examples are known to exist.

5,000 stamps from plate 2 were overprinted "Specimen" and distributed amongst various post offices.

4d RED
Total number issued 30,000,000 (125,000 sheets)

Break-down of plates:

Plate 3	13,800,000	(57,500 sheets)
4	16,200,000	(67,500 sheets)

6d LILAC
Total number issued 15,360,000 (64,000 sheets)

Break-down of plates:

Plate 3	11,040,000	(46,000 sheets)
4	4,320,000	(18,000 sheets)

9d BISTRE
Total number issued 1,573,200 (6,555 sheets)

Break-down of plates:

Plate 2	1,572,000	(6,550 sheets)
3	1,200	(5 sheets)

Notes: The 9d plate 3 were the five Registration sheets of which some were perforated and put into circulation. About 30 used copies and 3 unused examples have been recorded.

1s GREEN
Total number issued 6,241,200 (26,005 sheets)

Break-down of plates:

Plate 1 = Plate 2	6,240,000	(26,000 sheets)
Plate 2 = Plate 3	1,200	(5 sheets)

Notes: The 1s plate 2 = 3 were the five Registration sheets of which a few were unofficially perforated. 3 mint copies are known to exist.

5,000 stamps from plate 1 = 2 were overprinted "Specimen" and distributed amongst various post offices.

1865–67 SERIES WITH `LARGE WHITE CORNER LETTERS'

Watermark Emblem (except 4d which has Large Garter)

3d ROSE
Total number issued 10,198,800 (42,495 sheets)
Break-down of plates: All plate 4.

4d VERMILION
Total number issued 81,362,880 (339,012 sheets)

Break-down of plates:

Plate 7	8,280,000	(34,500 sheets)
8	10,800,000	(45,000 sheets)
9	10,080,000	(42,000 sheets)
10	2,760,000	(11,500 sheets)
11	13,200,000	(55,000 sheets)
12	15,842,880	(66,012 sheets)
13	12,000,000	(50,000 sheets)
14	8,400,000	(35,000 sheets)

6d LILAC
Total number issued 17,760,000 (74,000 sheets)

Break-down of plates:

Plate 5	14,880,000	(62,000 sheets)
6	2,880,000	(12,000 sheets)

9d STRAW
Total number issued 721,200 (3,005 sheets)
Break-down of plates: All plate 4.

Notes: Unused copies of the unissued plate 5 exist and examples must have come from the five Registration sheets printed, from which about 3 dozen stamps from the K, L, M, & N rows were perforated by Messrs. De La Rue in 1887 for insertion in twelve souvenir albums to be presented to members of the Stamp Committee. About twenty of these stamps were later returned to the Archives and replaced in the imprimatur sheet.

10d RED-BROWN
The 10d on Emblems watermark paper was printed in error whilst preparing the 1867 issue on Spray watermark paper. Only one or two sheets could have been produced and only 10 copies have been reported of which 7 were used in Constantinople.

1s GREEN
Total number issued 9,362,640 (39,011 sheets)
Break-down of plates: All plate 4.

Notes: Five Registration sheets of the 1s plate 5 with Emblems watermark were printed but never issued. Perforated examples with this watermark do not exist.

1867–80 SERIES WITH `LARGE WHITE CORNER LETTERS'

Watermark Spray of Rose – Designs as for 1865–67 series

3d ROSE
Total number issued 77,280,000 (322 sheets)

Break-down of plates:

Plate 4	2,641,200	(11,005 sheets)
5	23,158,800	(96,495 sheets)
6	17,880,000	(74,500 sheets)
7	8,400,000	(35,000 sheets)
8	8,400,000	(35,000 sheets)
9	8,400,000	(35,000 sheets)
10	8,400,000	(35,000 sheets)

6d LILAC (WITH HYPHEN)
Total number issued 14,400,000 (60,000 sheets)
Break-down of plates: All plate 6.
Notes: The 'Board' decided on the 24th of March, 1868 that this stamp should be issued in a brighter colour and from the 22nd of July, 1868 about 22,000 sheets (5,280,000 stamps) were issued in bright violet. This quantity is included in the figure given above for the total number issued.

6d MAUVE (WITHOUT HYPHEN)
Total number issued 27,841,200 (116,005 sheets)

Break-down of plates:

Plate 8	14,520,000	(60,500 sheets)
9	13,320,000	(55,500 sheets)
10	1,200	(5 sheets)

Notes: The 6d plate 10 were the five Registration sheets from which one or more sheets apparently got into circulation. About 5 or 6 used copies have been reported including one used on cover from Weymouth.

9d STRAW
Total number issued 5,315,520 (22,148 sheets)
Break-down of plates: All plate 4.
In addition, some 1,352 sheets (324,480 stamps) were produced but officially destroyed, comprising 230,660 stamps destroyed in December 1876 and the remainder destroyed during printing because of spoilage. A few of the sheets destroyed in December 1876 may have come from the unissued plate 5 (see notes under the 1865–67 9d issue). The total printing of this stamp was thus 23,500 sheets.

10d RED-BROWN
Total number issued 3,165,540 (13,189 (¾) sheets)

Break-down of plates:

Plate 1	3,164,340	(13,184 (¾) sheets)
2	1,200	(5 sheets)

In addition, 815 sheets (195,660 stamps) were produced but officially destroyed in December 1876, making a total printing for plate 1 of 14,000 sheets.
Notes: The 10d plate 2 were the five Registration sheets which are all believed to have been perforated and put into circulation. About

30 used copies have been recorded and one mint example was discovered in 1972. Another alleged unused copy exists in the Royal Collection but this may have had a cancellation removed.

1s GREEN
Total number issued 48,598,800 (202,495 sheets)

Break-down of plates:

Plate 4	18,480,000	(77,000 sheets)
5	13,318,800	(55,495 sheets)
6	8,400,000	(35,000 sheets)
7	8,400,000	(35,000 sheets)

Notes: One complete imperforate sheet of plate 4 overprinted "Specimen" has been broken up, and a single imperforate copy lettered TL has also been recorded.

2s BLUE
Total number issued 6,722,400 (28,010 sheets)

Break-down of plates:

Plate 1	6,721,200	(28,005 sheets)
3	1,200	(5 sheets)

Notes: At first, plate 1 was not aligned correctly which resulted in difficulty in perforating the stamps. After 2,005 sheets were printed, Messrs. De La Rue cut the plate into separate panes and refixed them to correct the problem. However, the fault had only affected part of the sheets and since Messrs. De La Rue had invoiced 1,953 sheets prior to the correction of this plate, it is assumed that part sheets equal in quantity to 52 complete sheets (12,480 stamps) were probably spoilt and destroyed. The quantity given for plate 1 does not take this into account.

The 2s plate 3 were the five Registration sheets, some of which were perforated and put into circulation. A very few used copies are known and a mint perforated example exists in the Royal Collection.

4,000 stamps from plate 1 were overprinted "Specimen" and distributed amongst various post offices. A complete imperforate sheet overprinted as such is known, together with an imperforate single lettered NG.

2s BROWN
Total number issued 77,620 (equal to nearly 323 half sheets)
Break-down of plates: All plate 1.
Notes: Originally, 1,000 sheets were printed of which after spoilage 967 full sheets and 28 half sheets were issued. After about four months the Post Office decided to discontinue this stamp and 157,820 examples (equal to over 657 half sheets) were officially destroyed. This leaves the total number put into circulation (plus a small residue of 4 sheets left over in stock) as given above. The facts indicate that about 1,000 mint copies exist.

1872 6d BUFF
Watermark Spray of Rose – Large white corner letters
Total number issued 9,601,200 (40,005 sheets)

Break-down of plates:

Plate 11 (Chestnut)	4,800,000	(20,000 sheets)
11 (Buff)	3,600,000	(15,000 sheets)
12 (Chestnut)	1,200	(5 sheets)
12 (Buff)	1,200,000	(5,000 sheets)

Notes: The five sheets of plate 12 in chestnut were Registration sheets, of which up to 4 sheets were apparently perforated and issued. A number of used examples have been recorded.

1873 6d GREY
Watermark Spray of Rose – Design as 1872 6d Buff
Total number issued 7,198,800 (29,995 sheets)
Break-down of plates: All plate 12.

1867–83 HIGH VALUES

Notes: Early printings of the stamps with Anchor watermark were on blued paper, but as printings progressed the paper became less blued and finally almost white owing to the variation in the composition of the prussate of potash. The blued and white papers are therefore really one issue and cannot be classified separately. A few of these stamps, especially those on Anchor paper, were used on telegrams.

5s ROSE
Watermark Maltese Cross – Perforation 15½ × 15 – Issued in sheets of 80
Total number issued 5,480,800 (68,510 sheets)

Break-down of plates:

Plate 1	3,920,000	(49,000 sheets)
2	1,560,400	(19,505 sheets)
4	400	(5 sheets)

Notes: The five sheets of plate 4 were Registration sheets and no perforated mint or used copies have yet been recorded.

5s ROSE
Watermark Large Anchor – Perforation 14 – Issued in sheets of 56
Total number issued 537,374 (9,596 sheets)
Break-down of plates: All plate 4.
In addition, some 404 sheets (22,626 stamps) were produced but destroyed in 1884, making a total printing of 10,000 sheets.

10s GREY-GREEN
Watermark Maltese Cross – Perforation 15½ × 15 – Issued in sheets of 80
Total number issued 242,000 (3,025 sheets)
Break-down of plates: All plate 1.

10s GREY-GREEN
Watermark Large Anchor – Perforation 14 – Issued in sheets of 56
Total number issued 224,000 (4,000 sheets)
Break-down of plates: All plate 1.

£1 BROWN-LILAC
Watermark Maltese Cross – Perforation 15½ × 15 – Issued in sheets of 80
Total number issued 242,000 (3,025 sheets)
Break-down of plates: All plate 1.

£1 BROWN-LILAC
Watermark Large Anchor – Perforation 14 – Issued in sheets of 56
Total number issued 112,000 (2,000 sheets)

Break-down of plates: All plate 1.

£5 ORANGE
Watermark Two Large Anchors – Perforation 14 – Issued in sheets of 56
Total number issued 246,826 (over 4,407 half sheets)
Break-down of plates: All plate 1.
Notes: This stamp was produced from the £5 Telegraph stamp by drilling out of each electro the word `Telegraph' and replacing it by the word `Postage'. It is interesting to note that only 1,500 sheets (84,000 stamps) were issued for the £5 Telegraph stamp which makes it considerably rarer than its postal counterpart.

1873–80 SERIES
WITH `LARGE COLOURED CORNER LETTERS'

2½d ROSY-MAUVE
Watermark Anchor – Issued in sheets of 192
Notes: These stamps were printed on paper which was blued chemically and normally used for fiscal purposes. Often the blueing was so slight that it appeared absent (the so-called white paper), especially on plates 2 and 3, but on plate 1 the blueing was usually more pronounced.
Total number issued 17,281,920 (90,010 sheets)

Break-down of plates:

Plate 1	6,720,000	(35,000 sheets)
2	6,720,000	(35,000 sheets)
3	3,840,000	(20,000 sheets)
4	960	(5 sheets)
5	960	(5 sheets)

Notes: The 2½d plates 4 and 5 on Anchor paper were printed as Registration sheets and although some of these may have been put into circulation, no mint or used perforated examples have yet been discovered.

The error of lettering LH-FL instead of LH-HL occurred on all printings from plate 2, thus 35,000 (one on each sheet) were originally created. However, since the error was not discovered until June, 1893 many of these must have been destroyed.

2½d ROSY-MAUVE
Watermark Orb – Issued in sheets of 192
Total number issued 91,198,080 (474,990 sheets)

Break-down of plates:

Plate 3	2,880,000	(15,000 sheets)
4	6,719,040	(34,995 sheets)
5	6,719,040	(34,995 sheets)
6	6,720,000	(35,000 sheets)
7	6,720,000	(35,000 sheets)
8	6,720,000	(35,000 sheets)
9	6,720,000	(35,000 sheets)
10	6,720,000	(35,000 sheets)
11	6,720,000	(35,000 sheets)
12	6,720,000	(35,000 sheets)
13	6,720,000	(35,000 sheets)
14	6,720,000	(35,000 sheets)
15	6,720,000	(35,000 sheets)

| 16 | 6,720,000 | (35,000 sheets) |
| 17 | 960,000 | (5,000 sheets) |

Notes: One complete imperforate sheet of plate 8 overprinted "Specimen" has been broken up.

2½d BLUE
Watermark Orb – Issued in sheets of 192
Total number issued 30,720,000 (160,000 sheets)

Break-down of plates:

Plate 17	5,760,000	(30,000 sheets)
18	6,720,000	(35,000 sheets)
19	11,520,000	(60,000 sheets)
20	6,720,000	(35,000 sheets)

Notes: There was no record kept of the quantity produced for plate 20, but the facts indicate that probably the usual 35,000 sheets were printed.

Plate 17 had already produced 5,000 sheets in rosy-mauve when the colour of this stamp was changed to blue. A further 30,000 sheets were then printed in the new blue colour, thus completing its quota of 35,000 sheets.

3d ROSE
Watermark Spray of Rose
Total number issued 74,400,000 (310,000 sheets)

Break-down of plates:

Plate 11	8,400,000	(35,000 sheets)
12	8,400,000	(35,000 sheets)
14	8,400,000	(35,000 sheets)
15	8,400,000	(35,000 sheets)
16	8,400,000	(35,000 sheets)
17	8,400,000	(35,000 sheets)
18	8,400,000	(35,000 sheets)
19	8,400,000	(35,000 sheets)
20	7,200,000	(30,000 sheets)

Notes: Plate 13 was defective and no stamps were printed from it.

It is possible that five Registration sheets were printed from plate 21 on Spray of Rose watermarked paper, since an imprimatur sheet does exist. However, no mint or used perforated examples have yet been discovered.

4d VERMILION
Watermark Large Garter
Total number issued 3,601,200 (15,005 sheets)

Break-down of plates:

| Plate 15 | 3,600,000 | (15,000 sheets) |
| 16 | 1,200 | (5 sheets) |

Notes: The 4d plate 16 were the five Registration sheets, but at least two of these sheets were perforated and issued. Some 8 used copies have been reported, but no mint perforated examples have yet been found.

4d SAGE-GREEN
Watermark Large Garter
Total number issued 12,000,000 (50,000 sheets)

Break-down of plates:

Plate 15	4,800,000	(20,000 sheets)
16	7,198,800	(29,995 sheets)
17	1,200	(5 sheets)

Notes: The 4d plate 17 were the five Registration sheets from which two sheets are believed to have been perforated and issued. A very few used copies are known to exist, mostly emanating from Bradford, but no mint perforated examples have yet been found.

One complete imperforate sheet of plate 15 overprinted "Specimen" has been broken up.

4d GREY-BROWN
Watermark Large Garter
Total number issued about 2,350,800 (9,795 sheets)
Break-down of plates: All plate 17.

6d BUFF
Watermark Spray of Rose
Total number issued 1,200 (5 sheets)
Break-down of plates: All plate 13
Notes: These were actually Registration sheets which were apparently all perforated and issued. About 18 used copies have been recorded, mostly used at Leeds, but no mint examples have yet been found.

6d GREY
Watermark Spray of Rose
Total number issued 37,198,800 (154,995 sheets)

Break-down of plates:

Plate 13	8,398,800	(34,995 sheets)
14	8,400,000	(35,000 sheets)
15	8,400,000	(35,000 sheets)
16	8,400,000	(35,000 sheets)
17	3,600,000	(15,000 sheets)

Notes: One complete imperforate sheet of plate 16 overprinted "Specimen" has been broken up.

8d ORANGE
Watermark Large Garter
Total number issued 4,801,200 (20,005 sheets)

Break-down of plates:

Plate 1	4,800,000	(20,000 sheets)
2	1,200	(5 sheets)

Notes: The 8d plate 2 were the five Registration sheets. No mint or used copies of these have yet been discovered.

8d PURPLE-BROWN
Watermark Large Garter
This stamp was prepared for use in July, 1876, but not issued and about 10,000 sheets of plate 1 were printed of which most were officially destroyed. However, a few mint copies have survived. This stamp was eventually issued in orange (see above).

1s GREEN
Watermark Spray of Rose
Total number issued 48,001,200 (200,005 sheets)
Break-down of plates:

Plate 8	8,400,000	(35,000 sheets)
9	8,400,000	(35,000 sheets)
10	8,400,000	(35,000 sheets)
11	8,400,000	(35,000 sheets)
12	8,400,000	(35,000 sheets)
13	6,000,000	(25,000 sheets)
14	1,200	(5 sheets)

Notes: The 1s plate 14 were the five Registration sheets from which possibly only one sheet was perforated and issued. Four used copies are known, mostly emanating from Greenock, but no mint perforated examples have yet been found.

1s ORANGE-BROWN
Watermark Spray of Rose
Total number issued 1,200,000 (5,000 sheets)
Break-down of plates: All plate 13.
Notes: No record was kept of the production of this stamp, but since there was no longer a great demand for a 1s. value owing to the introduction of a Telegraph stamp of the same duty, it may be safely assumed that there was only the one creation warrant, for 5,000 sheets, made out in September 1880.

POSTAGE STAMPS USED ON TELEGRAMS

When the Government took over the private Telegraph Companies in 1870, telegraph charges were mainly defrayed by the use of an embossed 1s. stamp similar in appearance to the embossed 1s. postage stamp of 1847, but the charges could also be paid by using ordinary postage stamps. Early in 1876 the Post Office introduced special telegraph stamps and the use of postage stamps was no longer permissible. On the 1st of November 1881 telegraph stamps were abolished altogether and from then on all telegrams were prepaid by the use of ordinary postage stamps. Consequently, certain post–1881 values (especially the 1s. denomination) had a considerable telegraphic usage and most of the stamps used on telegrams were eventually officially destroyed. In this catalogue the proportions and quantities quoted of postage stamps most frequently used for telegraphic purposes are calculated by comparing such denominations with the numbers sold of the official telegraph stamps issued prior to 1881. The use of the telegraph system started to decline after 1900 owing to the increasing use of the telephone.

1880–83 SERIES WITH `LARGE COLOURED CORNER LETTERS'

Watermark Imperial Crown – Designs as in 1873–80 series
Notes: The quantities produced from each plate in this series are not recorded, but some information is available on the total numbers sold for each value. The total quantities must therefore be taken as approximate and the break-down of plates have been estimated.

2½d BLUE
Total number issued 92,640,000 (386,000 sheets)

Break-down of plates:

Plate 21	30,240,000	(126,000 sheets)
22	31,200,000	(130,000 sheets)
23	31,200,000	(130,000 sheets)

3d ROSE
Total number issued 45,900,000 (191,250 sheets)

Break-down of plates:

Plate 20	15,900,000	(66,250 sheets)
21	30,000,000	(125,000 sheets)

Note: At least one quarter of these stamps were used on telegrams.

4d GREY-BROWN
Total number issued 13,248,000 (55,200 sheets)

Break-down of plates:

Plate 17	6,048,000	(25,200 sheets)
18	7,200,000	(30,000 sheets)

6d GREY
Total number issued 30,000,000 (125,000 sheets)

Break-down of plates:

Plate 17	13,200,000	(55,000 sheets)
18	16,800,000	(70,000 sheets)

Notes: When the 6d on 6d lilac was introduced in 1883 the remaining stock of plate 18 in grey was overprinted "I.R.Official" and these are included in the above total.

It is estimated that some 1,750,000 stamps from plate 17 and 1,250,000 stamps from plate 18 were used on telegrams.

1s ORANGE-BROWN
Total number issued 59,520,000 (248,000 sheets)

Break-down of plates:

Plate 13	31,920,000	(133,000 sheets)
14	27,600,000	(115,000 sheets)

Notes: At least one half of these stamps were used on telegrams.

`3d' SURCHARGED IN CARMINE ON 3d LILAC
Total number issued 14,400,000 (60,000 sheets)
Break-down of plates: All plate 21.
Notes: At least one quarter of these stamps were used on telegrams, and a few were used for revenue purposes.

`6d' SURCHARGED IN CARMINE ON 6d LILAC
Total number issued 9,600,000 (40,000 sheets)
Break-down of plates: All plate 18.
Notes: One example of this stamp exists with a double overprint and this was discovered by the author of this book in 1966.

At least one quarter of these stamps were used on telegrams, and a few were used for revenue purposes.

1880–81 NEW DESIGNS `WITHOUT PLATE NUMBERS'
Watermark Imperial Crown – No check letters (except for 1 d value)

½d GREEN
Total number issued 902,520,000 (3,760,500 sheets)

1d VENETIAN RED
Total number issued 1,462,584,000 (6,094,100 sheets)

1½d VENETIAN RED
Total number issued 49,248,000 (205,200 sheets)

2d ROSE
Total number issued 27,396,000 (114,150 sheets)
Notes: One imperforate copy overprinted "Specimen" has been recorded.

5d INDIGO
Total number issued 9,804,000 (40,850 sheets)
Notes: One imperforate copy overprinted "Specimen" has been recorded.

POSTAGE STAMPS USED FOR REVENUE PURPOSES
With the introduction of the 1881 1d lilac, penny postage stamps could also be used for revenue purposes and the words "Postage & Revenue" were incorporated in the stamp design. In February 1883 this inscription and usage was extended to all other values up to 2s.6d. The main demand for revenue usage at that time was for the 1d, 3d, 6d, 1s, and 2s.6d. denominations.

THE PARCEL POST
The Post Office introduced the Parcel Post on the 1st of August, 1883 and thus stamps used after that date may be found with parcel post obliterations. Since 3d was the minimum inland parcel post rate, values of 3d and over were mainly used.

1881 1d LILAC
Watermark Imperial Crown – No check letters in corners.
Total number issued 34,095,984,000 (142,066,600 sheets)
Breakdown of Dies:

Die I (14 dots in each corner)	495,984,000	(2,066,600 sheets)
Die II (16 dots in each corner)	33,600,000,000	(140,000,000 sheets)

Notes: It is estimated that about 1% of these were used for revenue purposes.

1883–84 HIGH VALUES
Watermark Large Anchor – Issued in sheets of 112
Notes: At first this issue was printed on paper blued for revenue purposes, but early in 1884 the blued paper was replaced by white paper. The actual quantities printed on blued paper are not available, although considerably less were produced than on the later white paper. The totals given below are therefore of the combined printings on blued and white paper. A few of these stamps were used on telegrams

2s.6d LILAC
Total number issued 10,325,392 (92,191 sheets)
Notes: A few of these stamps were used for revenue purposes.

5s ROSE
Total number issued 7,520,800 (67,150 sheets)
Notes: These stamps may be found perforated 12 but they were never issued and originate from parts of waste sheets sent to Somerset House for official reasons.

10s ULTRAMARINE
Total number issued 1,929,200 (17,225 sheets)

1884 £1 BROWN-LILAC
Watermark three Imperial Crowns – Issued in sheets of 80
Total number issued 360,160 (4,502 sheets)
Notes: A few of these stamps were used on telegrams.

1888 £1 BROWN-LILAC
Watermark three Orbs – Issued in sheets of 80 – Design as 1884 £1
Total number issued 80,800 (1,010 sheets)
Notes: This issue was actually an error of printing on fiscal paper. When the error was discovered the Post Office withdrew the remainder which had not already been circulated (probably some 10,000 stamps of the above total) and overprinted them "I.R. Official" for official use.
    A few of these stamps were used on telegrams.

1883–84 UNIFIED SERIES
Watermark Imperial Crown – Check letters in corners
Notes: All the following values (except the 9d) may be found imperforate or perforated 12. These were never issued and came from parts of waste sheets sent to Somerset House for official purposes.

½d SLATE BLUE
Design as 1880–81 ½d
Total number issued 949,920,000 (3,958,000 sheets)

1½d LILAC
Total number issued 57,240,000 (238,500 sheets)

2d LILAC
Total number issued 27,240,000 (113,500 sheets)

2½d LILAC
Total number issued 111,960,000 (466,500 sheets)

3d LILAC
Total number issued   42,480,000   (177,000 sheets)
Notes: At least one third of these stamps were used on telegrams or for revenue purposes.

4d DULL GREEN
Total number issued   15,960,000   (66,500 sheets)

5d DULL GREEN
Design as 1½d
Total number issued   12,000,000   (50,000 sheets)
Note: There were two Dies of the 5d of which only Die II was issued and represented in the above total. Die I (with a short line under 'd' of value instead of a dot) was prepared and some 2,500 sheets printed, but the plate cracked early in use and most of those already printed were officially destroyed, although a few mint copies are known to have survived.

6d DULL GREEN
Design as 2d
Total number issued   21,240,000   (88,500 sheets)
Notes: At least one third of these stamps were used on telegrams or for revenue purposes.

9d DULL GREEN
Design as 2½d
Total number issued   6,480,000   (27,000 sheets)

1s DULL GREEN
Design as 3d
Total number issued   54,000,000   (225,000 sheets)
Notes: At least four fifths of these stamps were used on telegrams or for revenue purposes.

1887–1900 "JUBILEE" ISSUE
Watermark Imperial Crown (£1 three Crowns)

½d VERMILION
Total number issued   13,494,216,720 (56,225,903 sheets)

½d BLUE-GREEN
Total number issued   2,605,146,600   (10,854,777 sheets)

1½d PURPLE AND GREEN
Total number issued   492,960,000   (2,054,000 sheets)

2d GREEN AND CARMINE
Total number issued   305,448,000   (1,272,700 sheets)

2½d PURPLE ON BLUE PAPER
Total number issued   469,920,000   (1,958,000 sheets)
Notes: One sheet printed on the gummed side was found at Southampton in 1904.

3d PURPLE ON YELLOW PAPER
Total number issued   527,040,000   (2,196,000 sheets)
Notes: It is estimated that about 45,000,000 of these stamps were used on telegrams or for revenue purposes.

4d GREEN AND BROWN
Issued in sheets of 80
Total number issued   222,000,000   (2,775,000 sheets)

4½d GREEN AND CARMINE
Issued in sheets of 80
Total number issued   82,000,000   (1,025,000 sheets)
Notes: This value was introduced in 1892 for use on parcels weighing two pounds, but in June 1897 this rate became obsolete and a large stock of 4½d stamps remained unused. For this reason the 4½d is more common mint than used and the majority of used copies are, of course, parcel cancelled.

5d DULL PURPLE AND BLUE
Total number issued   142,800,000   (595,000 sheets)
Notes: Two Duty Plates exist of the 5d value, of which probably some 100,000 sheets were of Duty Plate I and the rest Duty Plate II.

6d PURPLE ON RED PAPER
Total number issued   784,800,000   (3,270,000 sheets)
Note: It is estimated that about 75,000,000 of these stamps were used on telegrams or for revenue purposes.

9d PURPLE AND BLUE
Issued in sheets of 80
Total number issued   77,920,000   (974,000 sheets)
Notes: It is estimated that about 7,000,000 of these stamps were used on telegrams or for revenue purposes.

10d PURPLE AND RED
Issued in sheets of 96
Total number issued   33,465,600   (348,600 sheets)

1s GREEN
Total number issued   138,600,000   (577,500 sheets)
Notes: It is estimated that over 100,000,000 of these stamps were used on telegrams or for revenue purposes.

1s GREEN AND CARMINE
Total number issued   27,996,000   (116,650 sheets)
Notes: One sheet with inverted watermark was found at Liverpool in 1900.
    Very few of these stamps were used on telegrams, as the basic telegraph rate was changed from 1s to 6d in 1899, and this stamp was issued in 1900.

£1 GREEN
Issued in sheets of 80 – Design as 1884 £1
Total number issued   701,760   (8,772 sheets)
Notes: A few of these stamps were used on telegrams.

KING EDWARD VII

1902–10 DE LA RUE PRINTINGS
Watermark Imperial Crown (½ to 1s); Large Anchor (2s.6d to 10s); three Crowns (£1)

½d GREEN
Total number issued   18,524,101,680 (77,183,757 sheets)
Notes: 67,101,600 (279,590 sheets) of the above total were produced in special sheets of 240, half with inverted watermark, for use in Post Office Booklets.

1d RED
Total number issued   19,012,289,520 (79,227,837 sheets)
Notes: 103,524,960 (431,354 sheets) of the above total were produced in special sheets of 240, half with inverted watermark, for use in Post Office Booklets.

1½d PURPLE AND GREEN
Total number issued   297,518,400   (1,239,660 sheets)

2d GREEN AND CARMINE
Total number issued   287,701,440   (1,198,756 sheets)

2½d BLUE
Total number issued   603,649,200   (2,515,205 sheets)

3d PURPLE ON YELLOW PAPER
Total number issued   468,448,800   (1,951,870 sheets)

4d GREEN AND BROWN
Total number issued   312,208,080   (1,300,867 sheets)

4d ORANGE
Total number issued   96,727,200   (403,030 sheets)

5d DULL PURPLE AND BLUE
Total number issued   191,848,800   (799,370 sheets)

6d PURPLE
Total number issued   561,474,240   (2,339,476 sheets)
Notes: It is estimated that about 120,000,000 of these stamps were used on telegrams or for revenue purposes.

7d GREY
Total number issued   5,963,040   (24,846 sheets)

9d PURPLE AND BLUE
Issued in sheets of 80
Total number issued   51,010,560   (637,632 sheets)

10d PURPLE AND RED
Issued in sheets of 96
Total number issued   33,465,600   (348,600 sheets)

1s GREEN AND CARMINE
Total number issued   125,063,280   (521,097 sheets)

2s.6d PURPLE
Issued in sheets of 56
Total number issued   9,634,464   (172,044 sheets)

5s CARMINE
Issued in sheets of 56
Total number issued   4,343,472   (77,562 sheets)

10s BLUE
Issued in sheets of 56
Total number issued   1,513,680   (27,030 sheets)

£1 GREEN
Issued in sheets of 40
Total number issued   804,880   (20,122 sheets)

1910 PREPARED FOR USE BUT NOT ISSUED – 2d TYRIAN PLUM

It was intended that this stamp should have been issued on the 6th of May 1910, but on that day the King died and practically all the stamps printed were officially destroyed. The few surviving copies include a complete sheet (except that one corner stamp is missing) owned by the General Post Office, a mint pair in the Royal Collection and some ten other known examples. One of these stamps was used on a letter to the Prince of Wales (later King George V) on the 5th of May 1910 and this is housed in the Royal Collection.

King Edward VII died on the 6th of May 1910 and although further provisional stamps bearing the King's portrait were produced between 1911 and 1913 by Messrs. Harrison & Sons and the Somerset House Printers, these were actually issued during the reign of King George V.

Following the King's death, Messrs. De La Rue handed over some of the printing plates to Messrs. Harrison & Sons and to the Somerset House Printers for printing the provisional issues and Messrs. De La Rue's contract for printing stamps ended on the 31st of December, 1910. Unfortunately, the new printers kept inadequate records of numbers of stamps printed and the Post Office Record Book ceased recording quantities at the end of 1908. Therefore, it is impracticable to supply numbers of definitive stamps issued after 1910.

The numbers issued or printed for commemorative sets up to modern times are known. Since most specialised catalogues record the quantities issued for the Queen Elizabeth period, it is pointless repeating them here, but for easy reference details are given for the commemorative sets issued until the end of the reign of King George VI.

1924/25 BRITISH EMPIRE EXHIBITION:
All values combined (17,000,000)

1929 POSTAL UNION CONGRESS:
½d (677,500,000), 1d (341,000,000), 1½d (751,250,000), 2½d (26,750,000), £1 (61,000)

1935 SILVER JUBILEE:
½d (353,400,000), 1d (150,400,000), 1½d (490,000,000), 2½d (14,200,000)

1937 CORONATION:
1½d (388,731,000)

1940 POSTAL CENTENARY:
½d (82,896,960), 1d (232,903,680) 1½d (40,412,800), 2d (121,065,120), 2½d (312,957,440), 3d (22,128,000)

1946 VICTORY:
2½d (307,832,500), 3d (43,085,700)

1948 ROYAL SILVER WEDDING:
2½d (147,500,000), £1 (419,628)

1948 CHANNEL ISLANDS LIBERATION:
1d (5,934,000), 2½d (5,398,000)

1948 OLYMPIC GAMES:
2½d (155,350,000), 3d (32,554,000), 6d (24,397,000), 1s (32,187,000)

1949 UNIVERSAL POSTAL UNION:
2½d (135,150,000), 3d (16,450,000) 6d (11,450,000), 1s. (11,400,000)

1951 FESTIVAL OF BRITAIN:
2½d (260,142,000), 4d (22,197,000)

THE OFFICIALS

1840 V.R. 1d BLACK
Watermark Small Crown –Imperforate –Letters "V.R." in upper corners

It was intended to issue this stamp with the first postage stamps of 1840 but although it was prepared for use and 3471 sheets were printed, it was never officially released. Of the original printing, 148 sheets were spoiled during production and 3302 officially destroyed on 25 January 1843. Of the residue of 21 sheets, one was sent to Rowland Hill on 18 April 1840 for use in cancellation trials, examples being known with Maltese Cross and concentric circles cancellations. 13 sheets were sent to Somerset House to be attached to circulars which were distributed to postmasters on 7 May 1840. Five sheets are unaccounted for. Used examples are known, probably having passed through the post in error, these and unused examples in collectors' hands are likely to come from the five sheets or from Post Office circulars.

GREAT BRITAIN STAMPS
OVERPRINTED FOR OFFICIAL USE

From 1882 to 1904 various Government departments overprinted stamps which were then current, for official use. These overprints consisted of "I.R. Official" (Inland Revenue), "O.W. Official" (Office of Works, "Army Official", "Govt. Parcels" (Government Parcels), "Board of Education", "R.H. Official" (Royal Household), and "Admiralty Official". The stamps overprinted were as follows:

1880–83	6d grey (plate 18), is orange-brown (plates 13 and 14).
1880–81	½d green.
1881	1d lilac.
1883–84	5s rose, 10s ultramarine.
1884	£1 brown-lilac watermark Crowns.
1888	£1 brown-lilac watermark Orbs.
1883–84	½d slate-blue, 1½d lilac, 2½d lilac, 6d dull green, 9d dull green, 1s dull green.
1887–1900	Jubilee all values except 3d and 4d, including the colour changes.
1902–10	Edward all values except the two 4d's, 7d and 2s.6d. The ½d was only overprinted on the blue-green shade.

It has not been possible to compile a complete listing of the numbers of stamps overprinted for official purposes, but set out below is the information that is so far known.

INLAND REVENUE

1901	6d purple on red paper (1887–1900 issue)
	120,000 (500 sheets)
1901	1s green and carmine (1887–1900 issue)
	2,400 (10 sheets)
1904	6d purple (1902–10 issue)

248 copies are known of which 6 are used and 242 are mint. Most of the used examples are postmarked May 14th 1904 and the mint includes a near complete sheet of 234 housed in the Post Office archives, a marginal pair and a single in the Royal Collection, and a block of four in the National Museum of Ireland at Dublin.

1902	10s blue (1902–10 issue) The Post Office archives holds 51 mint copies. Others exist.
1902	£1 green (1902–10 issue) The Post Office archives holds 35 mint copies. Others exist.

OFFICE OF WORKS

1901	½d blue-green (1887–1900 issue) 6,000 (25 sheets)
1902	5d dull purple and blue (1887–1900 issue) 12,000 (50 sheets) 949 were used.
1902	10d purple and red (1887–1900 issue) 800 (10 sheets of 80) 480 were used.
1903	10d purple and red (1902–10 issue) 240 (1,440 were printed in 15 sheets of 96, but 1,200 were officially destroyed. 134 were used.

ARMY OFFICIAL

1903	6d purple (1902–10 issue)

Number printed 480,000 (2,000 sheets). The bulk of this printing was officially destroyed.

GOVERNMENT PARCELS

1897	1d lilac "overprint inverted" error 240 (1 sheet)

Notes: This is the only recorded instance of an inverted overprint on a British stamp for use in Great Britain.

1900	1s green and carmine (1887–1900) 36,000 (150 sheets)

BOARD OF EDUCATION

1902	5d dull purple and blue (1887–1900 issue) 5,520 (66,000 were printed, 60,480 were officially destroyed)
1902	1s green and carmine (1887–1900 issue) 2,400 (33,000 were printed, 30,600 were officially destroyed)
1902–04	5d dull purple and blue and 1s green and carmine (1902–10 issue)

The majority of these two values were destroyed on the 14th of May 1904 when the general issue of the Officials ceased. The 1s was never officially issued. Very few of the 5d were issued. However, one or two of the 1s were used by some high official and a very few of the 5d were also used. The Post Office archives holds 114 mint copies of the 1s value.

ROYAL HOUSEHOLD

No information available.

ADMIRALTY OFFICIAL

No information available.

GREAT BRITAIN STAMPS OVERPRINTED FOR USE IN OTHER COUNTRIES

Although prior to 1880 British stamps had been used in many countries apart from Great Britain, Cyprus was the only country to actually overprint the stamps with the name of their country. During the 1880's this practice was adopted by six other countries (i.e. Bechuanaland, British East Africa, British Levant, Mafeking, Oil Rivers Protectorate, and Zululand), and in 1907 Morocco Agencies also began overprinting British stamps. Most of the British Levant stamps were only surcharged with a new currency and it was not until 1905 that they overprinted the stamps 'Levant'. In later years other countries have overprinted Great Britain stamps, but the information given below is confined to the period covered by this book 1840 to 1910. The stamps of Great Britain overprinted by the various countries were as follows:

1858–69	1d Red (plates 174, 181, 184, 193, 196, 201, 205, 208, 215, 216, 217, 218 and 220).
1870	½d Red (plates 12, 15 and 19).
1873–80	2½d rosy-mauve (plates 14 and 15), 4d sage-green (plate 16), 6d grey (plate 16), is green (plate 13).
1881	1d lilac
1883–84	2s.6d lilac, 5s rose.
1883–84	2½d lilac, 5d dull green.
1887–1900	Jubilee all values to 1s except 1½d, 4½d, and 1s green and carmine.
1902–10	Edward all values to 10/– except 7d and 9d.

Unfortunately, the totals of the stamps so overprinted are not known for all the countries, but the information that is available is indicated below.

BECHUANALAND

1881 1d lilac *Numbers not known*	
1887–1900 Jubilee ½d vermilion, ½d blue-green, 2d, 3d, 4d, 6d, 1s green	*Numbers not known*
1902–10 Edward ½d (blue-green and yellow-green), 1d, 2½d	*Numbers not known*

BRITISH EAST AFRICA

1881	1d. lilac	1,440 (6 sheets)
1887–1900	Jubilee	
	2d	1,440 (6 sheets)
	5d	780 (3 sheets)

BRITISH LEVANT

1883–84	2s.6d lilac	*Number not known*
1883–84	2½d lilac, 5d dull green	*Numbers not known*
1887–1900	Jubilee 2d vermilion	6,000 (25 sheets)
	2½d, 5d, 10d	*Numbers not known*
1902–10	Edward all values (including both 4d colours) except 7d, 9d, 10s and £1	*Numbers not known*

CYPRUS

1858–69	1d Red (plates 174, 181, 184, 193, 196, 201, 205, 208, 215, 216, 217, 218 and 220) total about	480,000 (2,000 sheets)
1870	½d Red (plates 12, 15 and 19) total	68,640 (143 sheets of 480)
1873–80	2½d rosy-mauve (plates 14 and 15) total 319,584	(16,642 sheets of 192)
	4d sage-green (plate 16)	13,440 (56 sheets)
	6d grey (plate 16)	3,360 (14 sheets)
	1s green (plate 13)	2,880 (12 sheets)

MAFEKING

1881	½d lilac	3,600 (15 sheets)
1887–1900	Jubilee ½d vermilion	6,000 (25 sheets)
	2d	2,400 (10 sheets)
	3d	1,440 (6 sheets)
	4d	2,320 (29 sheets of 80)
	6d	1,680 (7 sheets)
	1s green	570 (2³/₈ sheets)

MOROCCO AGENCIES

1902–10   Edward all values (including both 4d colours) except 3d, 7d, 9d and £1. The ½d was only overprinted on the yellow-green shade *Numbers not known*

OIL RIVERS PROTECTORATE

1881	½d lilac	33,360(278 half sheets)
1887–1900	Jubilee 1d vermilion	33,600 (280 half sheets)
	2d	33,480 (279 half sheets)
	2½d	57,000 (475 half sheets)
	5d	33,540 (279 half sheets +1¼ sheet)
	1s green	6,720 (56 half sheets)

ZULULAND

		Numbers sold
1881	1d lilac	459,776(1,915+ sheets)
1880–84	5s rose	998 (nearly 9 sheets of 112)
1887–1900	Jubilee ½d vermillion	268,224 (1,117+ sheets)
	2d	31,987 (133+ sheets)
	2½d	28,544 (118+ sheets)
	3d	11,949 (49+ sheets)
	4d	20,250 (253+sheets of 80)
	5d	6,428 (26+ sheets)
	6d	11,405 (47+ sheets)
	9d	3,701 (46+sheets of 80)
	1s green	4,654 (19+ sheets)

PROTECTIVE UNDERPRINTS

The following quantities of line-engraved stamps were officially underprinted (under the gum) by Messrs. Perkins, Bacon & Co. for the various companies in the period November 1872 to the end of 1877. It must be remembered, that in addition to those listed some were officially and unofficially both underprinted (under and over the gum) and overprinted before and after this period by Messrs. Perkins, Bacon & Co. and by the private firms using them, whilst Messrs. De La Rue officially underprinted certain surface-printed issues.

O.U.S.

| J. & C.
BOYD & CO.
7 FRIDAY ST. | W. H. SMITH
AND SON,
186, STRAND. | COPESTAKE,
MOORE,
CRAMPTON,&CO.,
London. | COPESTAKE.
MOORE.
CRAMPTON & CO.
LONDON. | G. E. R. |

Protective underprints

OXFORD UNION SOCIETY (O.U.S.)

1d Red	420,720	(1,753 sheets)

J. & C. BOYD & CO.

1d Red	696,000	(2,900 sheets)

W.H. SMITH AND SON

1d Red	96,000	(400 sheets)
2d Blue	12,000	(50 sheets)

COPESTAKE, MOORE, CRAMPTON & CO

1d Red	1,968,000	(4,100 sheets of 480)
1d Red	1,374,720	(5,728 sheets)
1½d Red	76,080	(317 sheets)
2d Blue	144,000	(600 sheets)

GREAT EASTERN RAILWAY (G.E.R.)

1d Red	360,000	(1,500 sheets)

Notes: This comprises the whole of the printing for the Great Eastern Railway, whose stamps were underprinted between November 1873 and January 1877.

A SUMMARY OF THE NUMBERS OF ADHESIVE POSTAGE STAMPS ISSUED DURING THE REIGN OF QUEEN VICTORIA

The following numbers of adhesive postage stamps were issued in the period 1840 to 1900:

	Stamps	Sheets of Stamps
½d	19,552,079,640	78,133,089
1d	56,644,726,080	236,019,525
1½d	642,086,160	2,675,359
2d	696,690,960	2,902,879
2½d	813,720,000	3,535,500
3d	796,872,000	3,320,300
4d	415,670,640	3,581,961
4½d	82,000,000	1,025,000
5d	164,604,000	685,850
6d	1,010,759,480	4,288,962
8d	4,801,200	20,005
9d	92,009,920	1,032,708
10d	35,843,500	503,505
1s	411,295,260	1,972,937
2s	6,800,020	28,333
2s.6d	10,325,392	92,191
5s	13,538,974	145,256
10s	2,395,200	24,250
£1	1,496,720	19,309
£5	246,826	4,408
Totals	81,397,961,972	340,011,327

When Messrs. Perkins, Bacon & Co. finally completed their printing contracts for the Line-Engraved series on the 31st of December 1879, the Board of Trade stated that the numbers of line-engraved stamps produced by the firm (excluding wastage) were:

½d	1,600,276,320
1d	20,699,858,040
1½d	42,638,160
2d	338,540,280

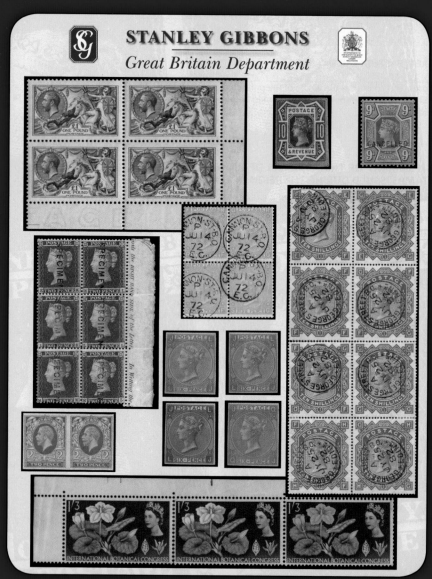

You may also like...